THE BLIND

CARTOONS BY FOXY

Cordee Leicester

First published in Great Britain in 1991
by Cordee 3a De Montfort Street, Leicester LE1 7HD

British Library Cataloguing in Publication Data

Fox, Alan
The Blind Probe : cartoons by Foxy
I. Title
797.122

ISBN 1871890853

Printed in Great Britain by BPCC Wheatons Ltd, Exeter

...ooh shit!...
© FOXY DESIGNS.

By the same author :

Cosmic Kayak Tours	(Cartoons)*
The Black Hole	(Cartoons)*
Run River Run	(Topo Guide to Classic UK Rivers, Diadem Books 1990)

* Denotes out of print

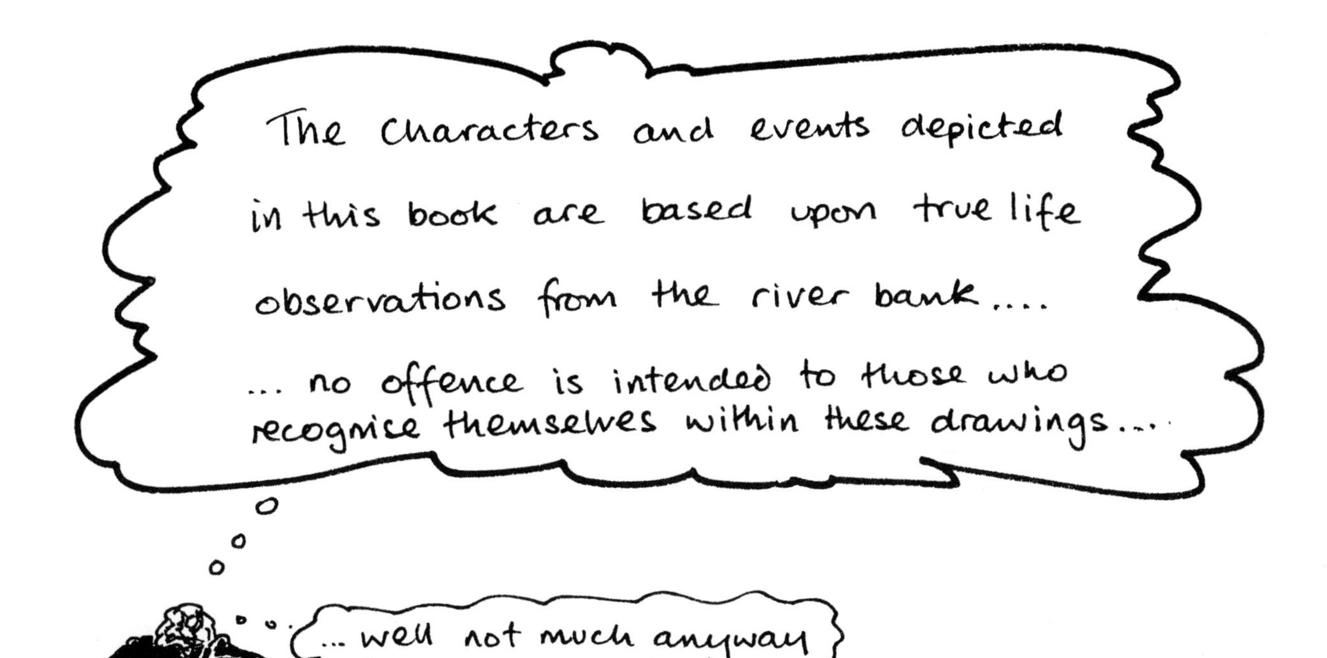
The characters and events depicted in this book are based upon true life observations from the river bank....
... no offence is intended to those who recognise themselves within these drawings....
... well not much anyway

..Suddenly, you find yourself at the front.....

... Autobiography of a blind Probe....
bye
oh s....
... the end is always the same.

The art of 'blind probing'.....

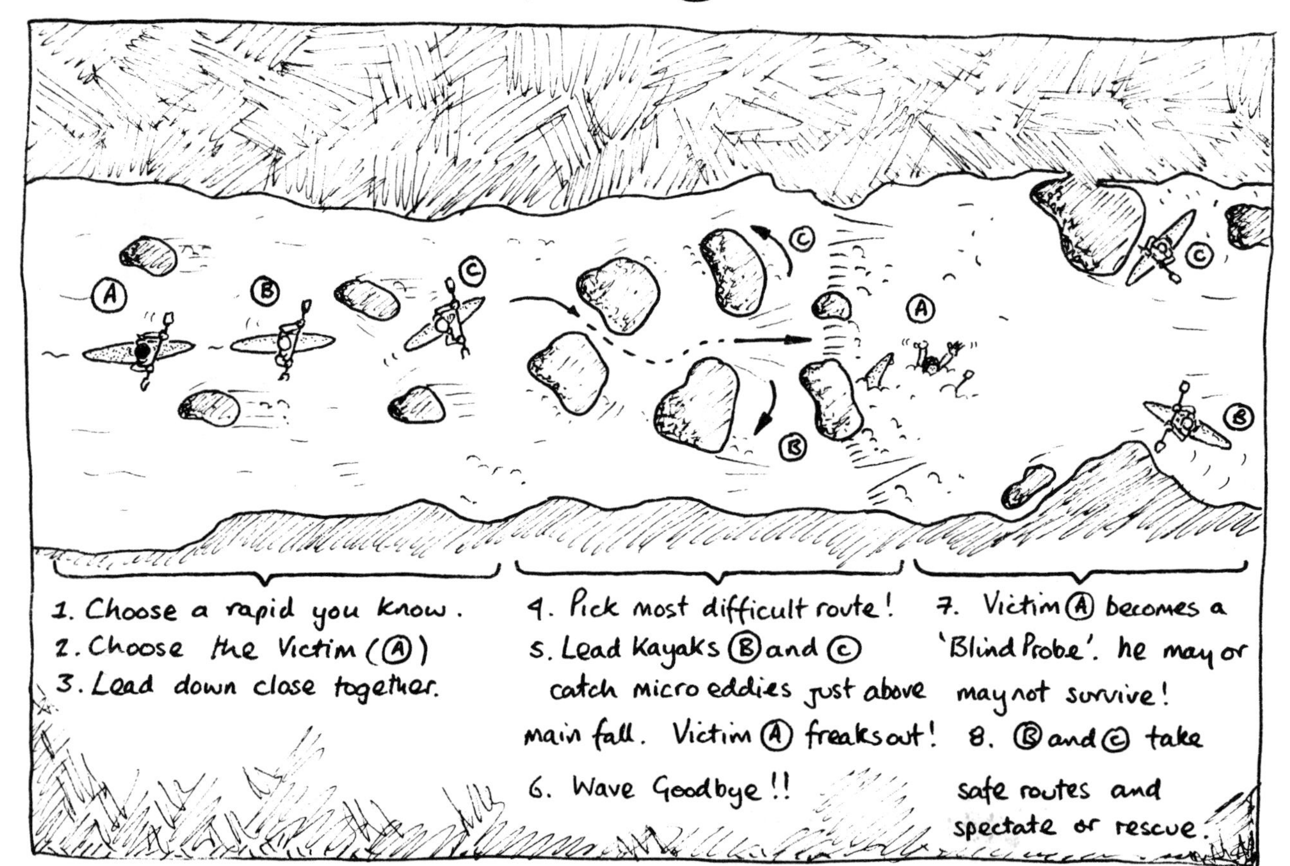

'Assumption' is the mother of all cock ups!...

... remember, If in doubt – get out ! ......

...The next drop is easy, I've done it before so there's no need to inspect....

...A Tale of two Probes......

We had already portaged one drop and the next series looked tricky but not too severe; three sharp drops within a short distance allowing very little time in between in which to recover.

I caught a breakout above the first fall and peered over. The drop dissappeared out of sight below. Jon paddled over and I motioned to him that a right hand route would be the best option... it was a mistake. Jons boat vanished as he slid over the fall only to reappear a split second later cartwheeling back into the fall.

I looked on in horror as the second loop spat the kayak out into the boiling water below. A second later Jon rolls up just in time to confront the second drop. Its a big bubbly stopper that holds him for a second before he breaks through into an eddy below. Jon turns and looks up at me, grinning, as he gives the thumbs up sign and yells,

"Come on down!"

I feel sick! how can I possibly improve upon that performance. I resign myself to fate and launch into the current. I try to aim further right than Jon's route and attempt to build up enough speed to ski jump the stopper. No luck, the fall is on too much of a slope, and I plunge down into the stopper. Thud! The boat strikes a rock stopping me dead, knees groan in agony, ankles twist in pain. Slowly I topple sideways into the fall.

The first few seconds bracing in the hole didn't seem too bad until I realised that I was slowly being sucked backwards deeper into the fall.

The rear deck catches and I flip backwards, "oh shit!", another flip follows but this time the kayak rises and I stay still as my kneebraces come unstuck and I fall out of the boat. As the kayak lands I catch the end toggle and we're swept out towards the second drop.

.. The boat looped leaving me upside down....
!?
...there was more to follow....

I emerge below, this time downstream of the kayak. Seconds later I'm swept onto the upstream side of a central rock, the kayak laden with water follows crushing me against the rock forcing me under, hydraulically crucified in mid stream. All that Jon can see are two hands pathetically waving above the surface trying to force the kayak off.

The kayak swings around and slides off, I follow, my relief however is shortlived as the third and final drop, a fifteen foot slide onto a rock ledge, looms up. Over I go crashing down, the kayak, following behind lands on top and then I'm floating out into the plunge pool – no more pain.

Jon appears, looking concerned, "You all right foxy?"

"F***......" I reply as I limp towards the bank, breathless, bruised and mentally trashed.

..It was THE END!

...Innocently in search of pleasure, naively heading into total danger...
...and so I said `its highly unlikely that you would get stuck in a canyon with an unrunnable rapid ahead and no possible portage'... no sense of adventure, some people are just too cautious nowadays...

... deja vu ...

Advice to International boaters:

" In Britain we call kayaks, canoes and we call canoes, canadians.

Confused? – you will be!

This can cause all sorts of problems ....

Booking a flight....

... The Travel Agent....

I'd like to take a kayak with me....

a canoe!

..a what?...

oh "   "

no Im sorry its too large.

an alternative approach...

... The response..

can you take a surfboard?..

"   " ...oh yes, no problem

ok, book a Surf 'KAYAK' on my ticket please

certainley sir

thats the concept dealt with, I'll worry about the details later...

FOXY©

Some white water safety tips....

Following the advice given below you should be able to avoid most of the unpleasant incidents that can arise from canoeing....

1. Always have a good excuse ready in case someone asks you to go paddling.
2. Stay at home! (avoids most problems, including the world!)
3. Don't go anywhere near water (the temptation may be too great!)
4. If you find yourself near the water feign 'sudden death'.
5. Be ready to say "I told you so" when anyone recounts an epic from a trip you avoided.
6. Take up a more sedate sport (like part time study, cartooning etc.)
7. Take more notice of your spouse (?!) (well maybe not!...)
8. Sell all your canoe kit and watch videos instead:

A word of Advice....

L

WET WILLIES CANOE KIT LTD.
CARE OF YOUR BOUYANCY AID.

This product will degrade if:
1. It is exposed to sunlight
2. It is compressed
3. Subjected to rough use
4. Stored in damp conditions

..In short, if you want this product to perform at its best then keep it locked away in a dark dry cupboard and in no circumstances ever take it canoeing!

This does not affect your statutory rights

RAPIDS WITH A REPUTATION : ✱ The 'graveyard'.

River features #1: ... dangerous rocks....

The First Canoe

HARMONIOUS RELATIONSHIPS - On the race course!
FOXY ©

HARMONIOUS RELATIONSHIPS #1.

"THIS IS MY EDDY SQUIRT FACE!"

...I dont wanna die...
...The Fear of Falling...
(I don't wanna die!)
...it comes to us all sooner or later.....

...continued...

Coming to terms with Gravity is perhaps the only pre-requisite for running waterfalls...

...that...
..and the concept of
landing!....

...wish I'd stayed at home!..
...come on down!...
FOXY©91

Spot the difference!

1. The novice waterfall kayaker.

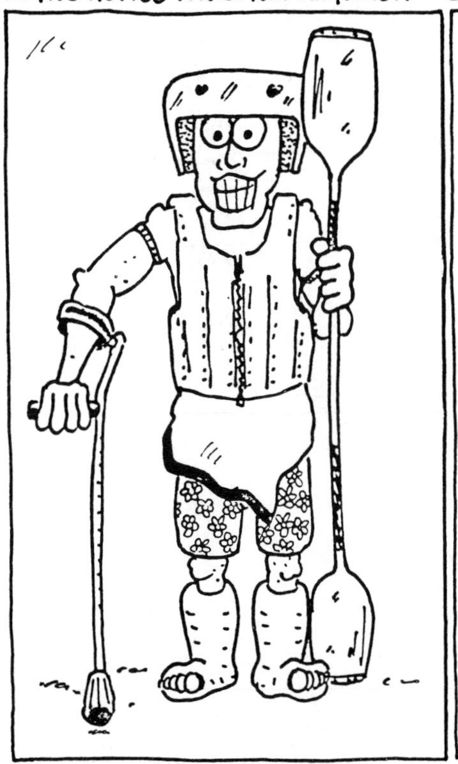

2. The expert waterfall kayaker.

...The longer you spend reading 'Kayak', the less time you spend getting trashed...
...suits me fine!
KAYAK
FOXY©

... and for those really big falls...

AIR PILLOW INC.

What happened next.....

.... A new dimension in Vertical kayaking .....

(or the shape of things to come.)

...when I said "it's not worth getting changed for" I meant....
Fozy ©

The fear of Landing...

Its at this point that you lose all orientation of mind and body, 9 times out of 10 your mind tells you that you're going back into the stopper....

...do I bail out or wait 5 seconds...

To ensure that you're not left at the top to run the fall on your own, quickly thrust your camera into someone else's hands and say....

... Always look before you leap!....

Much Ado....

...Observations from the river bank.

F = ma and the conservation of momentum.

Dont push me !...

This is my land piss off!
No Underprivileged people
No Admittance
Strictly private
No Canoeing
Fishing only
Narrow minded indigenous sheep shaggers only
Very priviliged people only.
...ok you bastards come and get me!...

suddenly....

CLICK
CLICK
CLICK
CLICK
Kill
CLICK
CLICK
...Just kidding..really...

BOOM

HARMONIOUS RELATIONSHIPS : Access......

The only catch of the day.....

"... Thats right folks, guess the new revolutionary product from WildWater and you could win a holiday for two in Pateley Bridge or...."
WILDWATER

New Products: the Explorer "Yuppie".

Surfing Stoppers #2: The 'hf.[T.M.]' kayak song...

Why? when its taken so long to get changed.....

... you suddenly
get desperate
for a sh** .....

essential hotdogging 

essential hotdogging

essential hotdogging ※ 3

...Bits of trips....

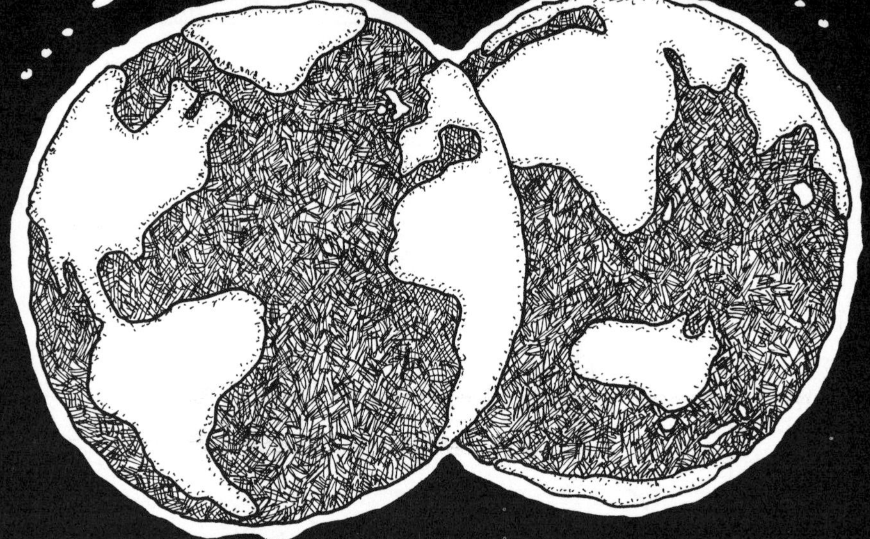

...This way

The ease of travelling in Chile....
$
TAXI
...Bio Bio?..

On the way to the Rio Bio Bio....

On Lava South : ... it was a grade 4 ferry glide to the other side, and if you didn't make it - it would be bad! ... halfway across my paddles snapped... it was BAD!
This is bad, very bad!...
...and will probably get worse.
This way out

Essential Supplies for a weekend away....

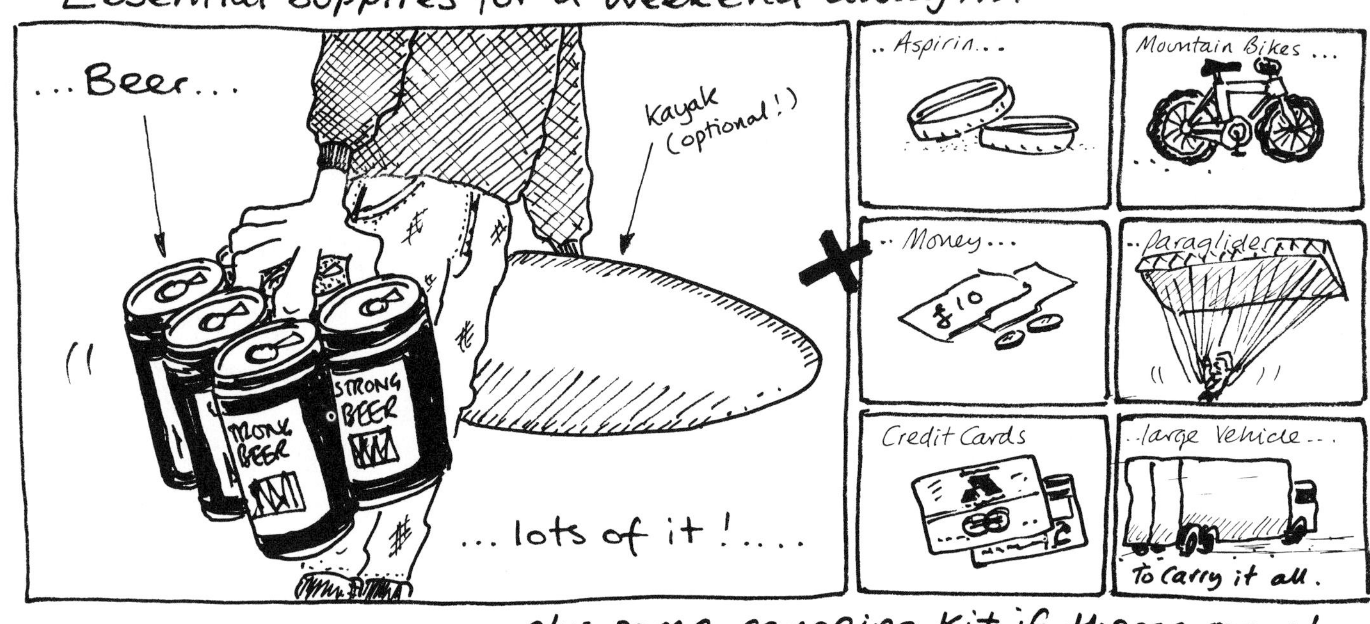

... plus some canoeing kit if theres room!...

... in the worlds 'deepest' canyon....

Ganga flow on

... a short trip to India ....

The travelling is more horrendous than the river....

... early on the Bhagarathi....

... the awareness that soloing brings...

Some Influence at the confluence....

.. it was time to float away...

... Ganga flow on....

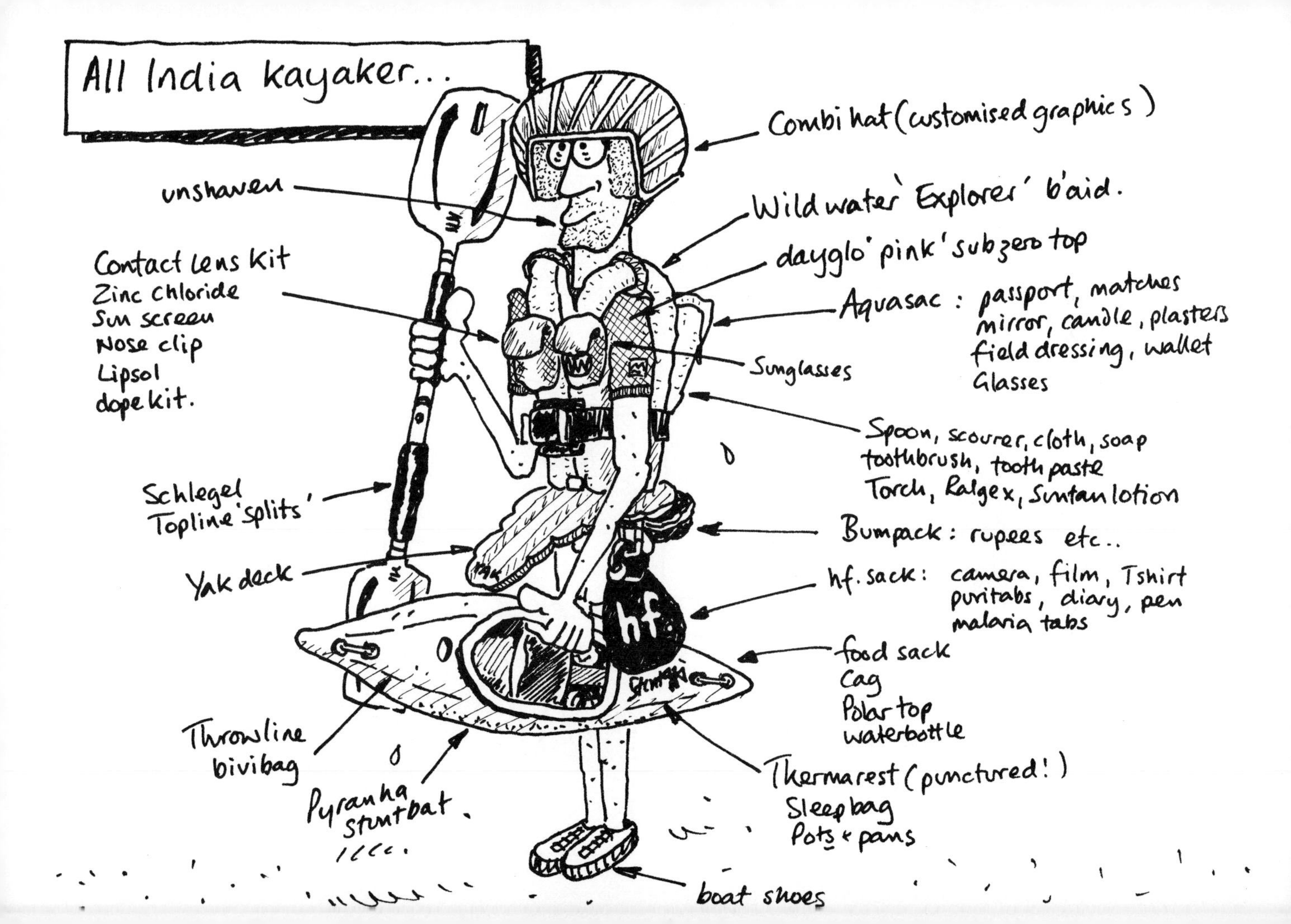

All India kayaker...
Combi hat (customised graphics)
unshaven
Wild water 'Explorer' b'aid.
dayglo 'pink' sub zero top
Contact lens kit
Zinc chloride
Sun screen
Nose clip
Lipsol
dope kit.
Aquasac: passport, matches
mirror, candle, plasters
field dressing, wallet
Glasses
Sunglasses
Spoon, scourer, cloth, soap
toothbrush, tooth paste
Torch, Ralgex, Suntan lotion
Schlegel
Topline 'splits'
Bumpack: rupees etc..
Yak deck
hf. sack: camera, film, Tshirt
puritabs, diary, pen
malaria tabs
hf.
food sack
Cag
Polar top
waterbottle
Throwline
bivibag
Pyranha
stuntbat
Thermarest (punctured!)
Sleepbag
Pots & pans
boat shoes

Photos from a solo kayak trip....

...Self portrait...

Some points about solo kayaking:

1: It can be dangerous.
2: It can be lonely
3: Who's gonna take your photo?
4: You absorb more of the local life.
5: No one tells you what to do.

Toke and Chunder River Tales

"True stories from the 1989 Zambezi Kayak Expedition...."

Smoke and Thunder River
ZAMBEZI
kayak expedition

So, just how dangerous are these crocs...?
AMMO
Fozy

..In the beginning.......

... and one day these two kayakers came paddling down the river... of course we scared them sh..tless.., I hadn't had so much fun since I ate someones grandmother.. and I hear that they are [illegible] back that should be fun.

Dad, tell me the one about the two kayakers again.....

CANOE PAIR TAME MIGHTY BATOKA GORGE

'The Zambezi? You need skilled medical attention mate. They have crocodiles there!' 'Of course they don't. Can't swim up rapids, can they?'

By hook, crook, and other devious means we found ourselves several months later standing aghast on the Victoria Falls Gorge. The first glimpse of the Zambezi caused instantaneous cranial explosion. The river, 1,800m wide, plunged 100m over the Falls and then squeezed itself into one twentieth of its previous width, transforming itself into a monstrous green snake, writhing and plunging its way down the hairpin gorge, sheet basalt walls soaring darkly either side. Over the last 150 million years natural erosion of faults in the basalt has caused the Falls to move gradually upstream, leaving behind this immense, impenetrable, inaccessible gorge — 'One of the Dark places of the Earth'. The kayaking was equally mind-blowing: Victoria Falls Gorges and the Batoka Gorge, separated in name only, contained what an American raft company calls '. . . the most exciting river in the world.'

572 killed by wild animals

ZIMBABWE: Wild animals killed 572 people last year, police revealed yesterday. Of the victims 544 were killed by crocodiles.

Apart from the hazards of the rapids, crocodiles also proved to be a threat.

About 20 km before Sidinda Island, the pair encountered scores of large crocodiles, some longer than their four-metre kayaks.

..... Dom', 'more grub' Gribbons....

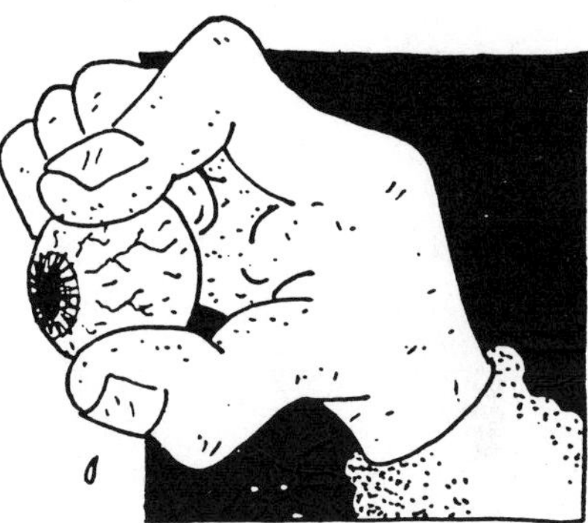

keeping an eye out for
Crocodiles!

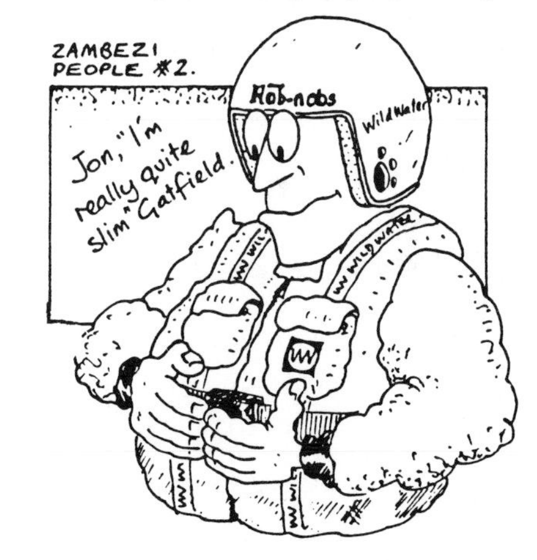

Dealing with crocodiles

..You can use a pea shooter

or offer them a sweet, or...

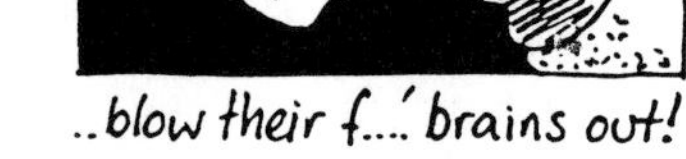

..blow their f...' brains out!

... meanwhile, despite the hardships of expedition life (?!) there was still time for romance to blossom! ...

...Mating season begins (scene: Victoria Falls at Moonlight...)

....mating season suspended.
(better luck next time Jon!)

.... continuous white water in the natural beauty

One to Ten...

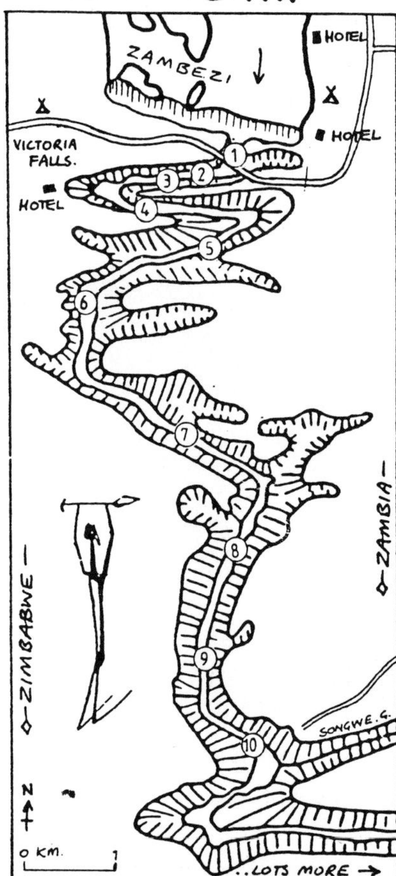

Rapid N°1: 'The boiling pot'...
..bigger and boilier than it looks!
Rapid N°2: 'Thunder Waves'....
... big smooth surfing waves.
Rapid N°3: Good lead in, then all hell breaks loose! long run and down to 'dead mans' corner.
Rapid N°4: a nice little 50/50 rapid.
Rapid N°5: "Who dares, gets trashed The road to Nirvana lies down the middle. Try it, you'll like it!
Rapid N°6: Whirlpools galore.
Rapid N°7: Very long and very meaty.
Rapid N°8: Big and Bouncy.
Rapid N°9: Awesome. Sneak routes In high flows. Easy portage.
Rapid N°10: Roller Coaster Finish.

The most incredible river trip in the world begins at the base of the Victoria Falls, "The Smoke that Thunders". From the first days ration of ten big river drops through a week of whitewater and scenery, the Zambezi is in a class all its own.

ZAMBEZI WHITEWATER CLASSIFICATION

Pleasing warm waters; the Zambezi River lies in a very steep, remote gorge, with big drops and relatively calm pools below each rapid. The Zambezi has the reputation to fluctuate its water levels throughout a given year. Thus at higher water levels the river moves much faster through these calm pools.

The ultimate river expedition! One hundred kilometres of the challenge, intrigue and romance of the Zambezi river gorges: superb rapids, spectacular flora and fauna, natural history, interesting cultural contacts with Zambezi fishermen

FOR YOUR INFORMATION

HIGH WATER SEASON: March and April.

LOW WATER SEASON: Mid-July to December

The rest of the River....

ZAMBIA

Livingstone

Boiling Pot

Victoria Falls

BATOKA GORGE

Kalomo R.

Zambezi River

DEVIL'S GORGE

Lake Kariba

RAPIDS ALL THE WAY!

ZIMBABWE

ANGOLA ZAMBIA Lake Kariba Zambezi R. NAMIBIA ZIMBABWE BOTSWANA MOZAMBIQUE SOUTH AFRICA Atlantic Ocean Indian Ocean

FROM 'RIVER GODS' A BOOK OF EPICS.

"The adventure, the white-water, the scenery and the challenge – that's the Zambezi ..YEAH MAN!..."

of the zambezi gorges.

A happening on N°4:

Route to avoid trashing

A 'bad' place to be!

oh sh...!

"On the last day every rapid had my name written on it, however N°4 was trivial compared to N°5, now that was one hell of a trashing!"

ZAMBEZI PEOPLE ✱3. ANXIOUS ANNE!

I was paddling down this rapid and the fear of crocodiles just threw me in, all I could think about was the crocs just waiting to take a big bite.

a river adventure.....

As our boats float the peaceful waters between the rapids, many incredible sights are witnessed. The basalt cliffs, towering above, stimulate the imagination as to the creation of this historic place. Perhaps you will be rewarded with a glimpse of one of the many bird species found nesting in the vicinity – the Black Eagle, the Hamerkop, the very rare Taita Falcon or the ever popular Fish Eagle. All around is the stark beauty of the Zambezi gorges. Then, of course, there is the unrivalled spectacle of the Victoria Falls when seen from the Boiling Pot

During the hair-raising trip the intrepid adventurers:

* picked their way between four-metre crocodiles.
* steered clear of huge hippos - responsible for more river deaths than any other Zambezi animal.
* narrowly avoided being blown out of the water by blundering explosives engineers building a dam.
* made a film of their exciting exploits to be shown on BBC.

The dam currently under construction will provide much-needed electricity but "will completely destroy a unique part of the world", said Les.

and then, into 'croc alley'!....
...I am your worst nightmare!
sobek

Same old boring rafts every day
I could do with a change, maybe a nice chunk of polyethylene!

WHERE IS......
Chibuku Gorge
Matt in a Zambezi Whirly....
The only way is down!
"Ghost Rider"...
pyranha
Wet dreams are made of this,
Pure fun on big water...

..back on the raft... bimbomania....

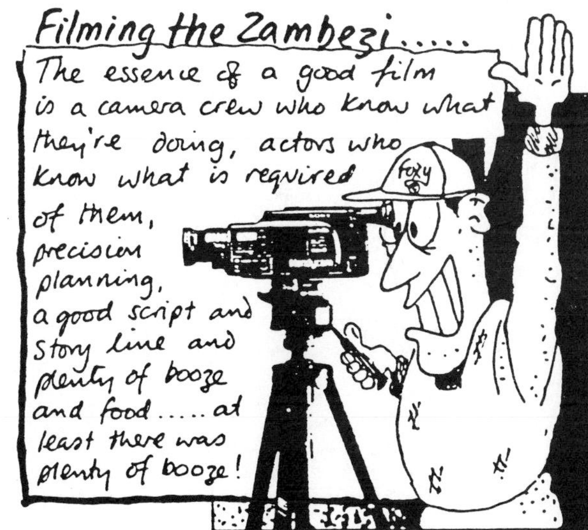
Filming the Zambezi.....
The essence of a good film is a camera crew who know what they're doing, actors who know what is required of them, precision planning, a good script and story line and plenty of booze and food..... at least there was plenty of booze!
Foxy

...a sneaky crocodile...

A crime in progress: Drowning the worlds most spectacular white water River Run .....

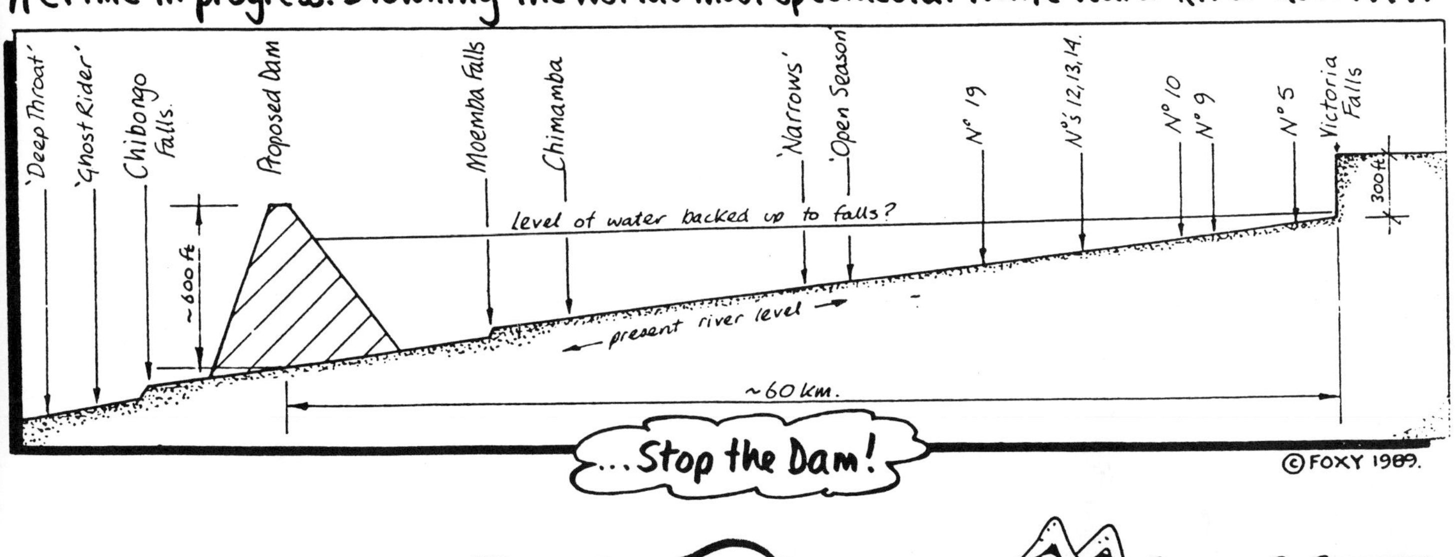

..and this croc' came towards me... and.... well I survived.... .... but not without a few scars....
Croc! my arse! .... only one small bloody mosquito bite!
BRAIN SURGEON
FOXY©

On Tour: ...another good doss spot....

.... There is no such thing as a quiet layby....

"THE SOBERING EFFECT OF A POLICE CAR"

The dreaded Himalayan 'Glof'!*...

(* Glof = Glacial lake outflow: sudden tidal waves have been known to sweep down rivers when glacial lakes have burst through ice walls.....)

~~Road~~ RIVER signs of Nepal....

"who tied the boats on?!"

TRUE STORIES: ANNE LEARNS TO ROLL!

Memories of the Brandenburgerache!

RIVER RATS .... hyping the impossible...

... The worlds ~~most~~ best river?...
descent.... by the worlds most
dangerous kayakers... The ~~most~~
... dangerous river.... highly
experienced.... drinkers... the...?
... the..... aha!
... a holiday for the lads!

FOXY©

RIVER RATS
※ The Guide Book Author....
"...Now was that river a grade 1, with grade 6 bits in between, or grade 6, with grade 1 bits in between...or... grade 2 to 3 but can be more difficult at times.... .... that'll do!"
:FOXY©:

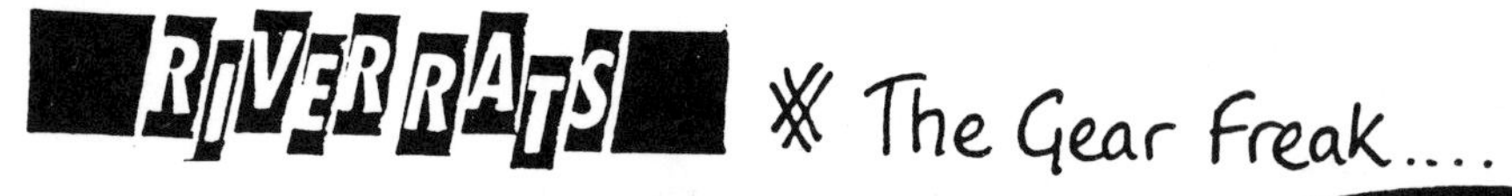

The Gear Freak....

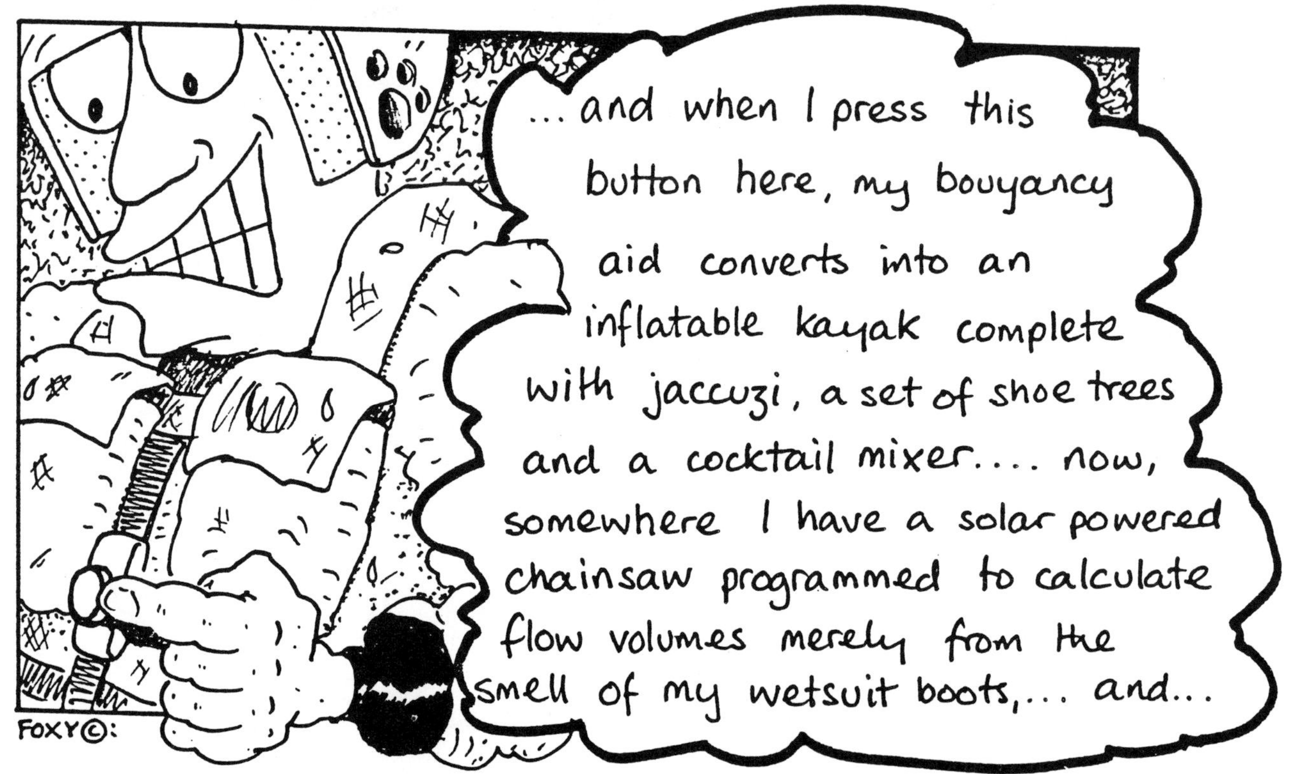

RIVER RATS ⁂ The Blind probe....

RIVER RATS
The Cameraman....
Wow! this will make a great photo!
where's the b***** rescue?...
FOXY©:

RIVER RATS
The Incentive....
No problem, I'll do anything as long as its on film.... fame and fortune here I come...
oops!...no film!
FOXY©

...oops!...
...never pose before the last breakout!...
FOXY©

RIVER RATS
Under pressure....
I don't think I can handle this... it's too much for me... It could be my last one... but then maybe I should, after all, it is...
...my round!
FOXY©

funny isn't it,.. someone does a fall, breaks a few ribs and is branded reckless and irresponsible, where as this guy kills himself on Niagara and is called a daredevil — its a pity some people dont think before putting pen to paper... where's their sense of Adventure and pushing the limits of acceprability so that others may learn?...
DAILY
FOXY ©

RIVER RATS
Safety Cover....
..and if he doesn't need a rescue by the time I get there, he sure will when I've finished with him!....
FOXY©

FOXY ©.
... temptation...

RIVER RATS
Making Movies..
...now, from the top again!... ..and this time keep to the script, we don't want a good story ruined by the facts....
FOXY©.

TECHNIQUE.
FOXY©

TECHNIQUE.
TRYING TO AVOID THE INEVITABLE
FOXY©

TECHNIQUE. 'NEGATIVE BOUYANCY'

TECHNIQUE · WATERFALL JUMPING

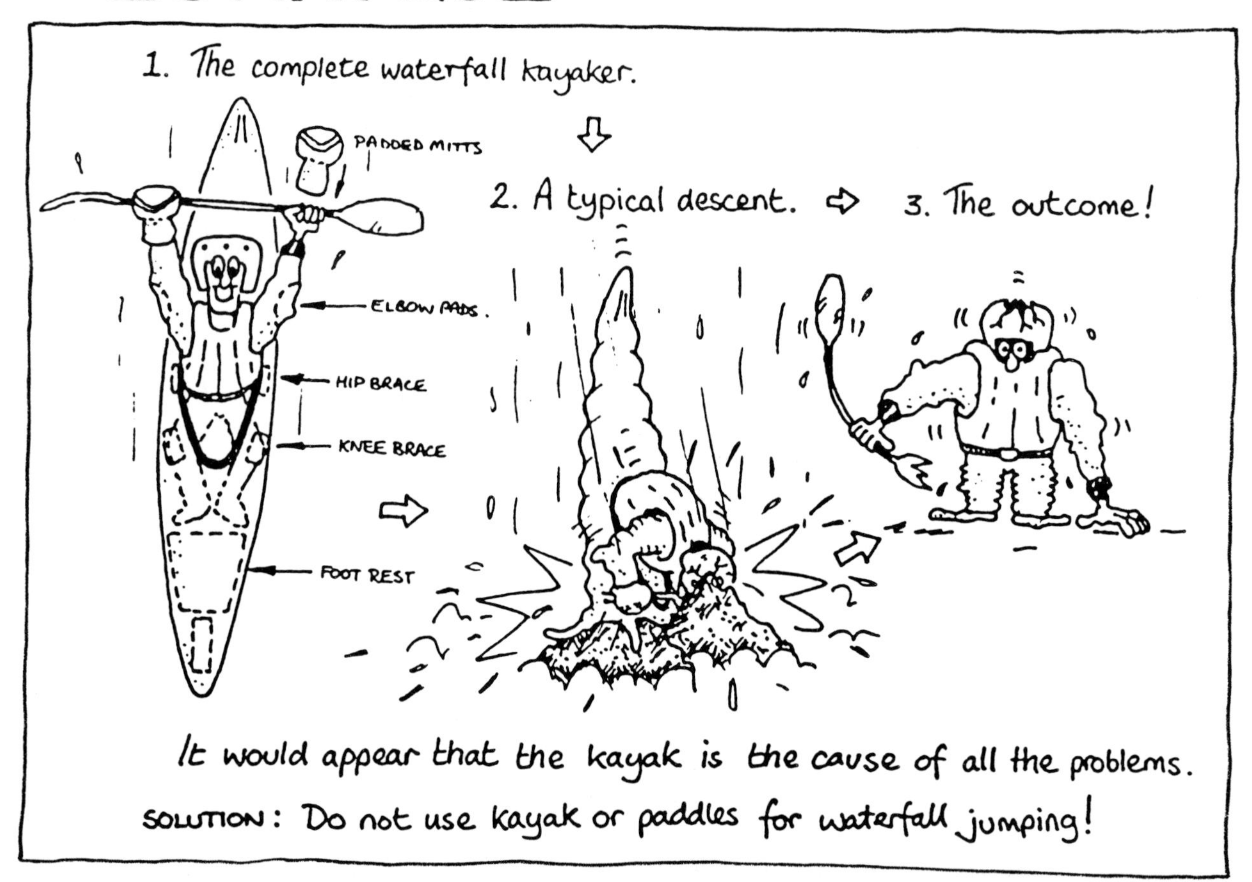

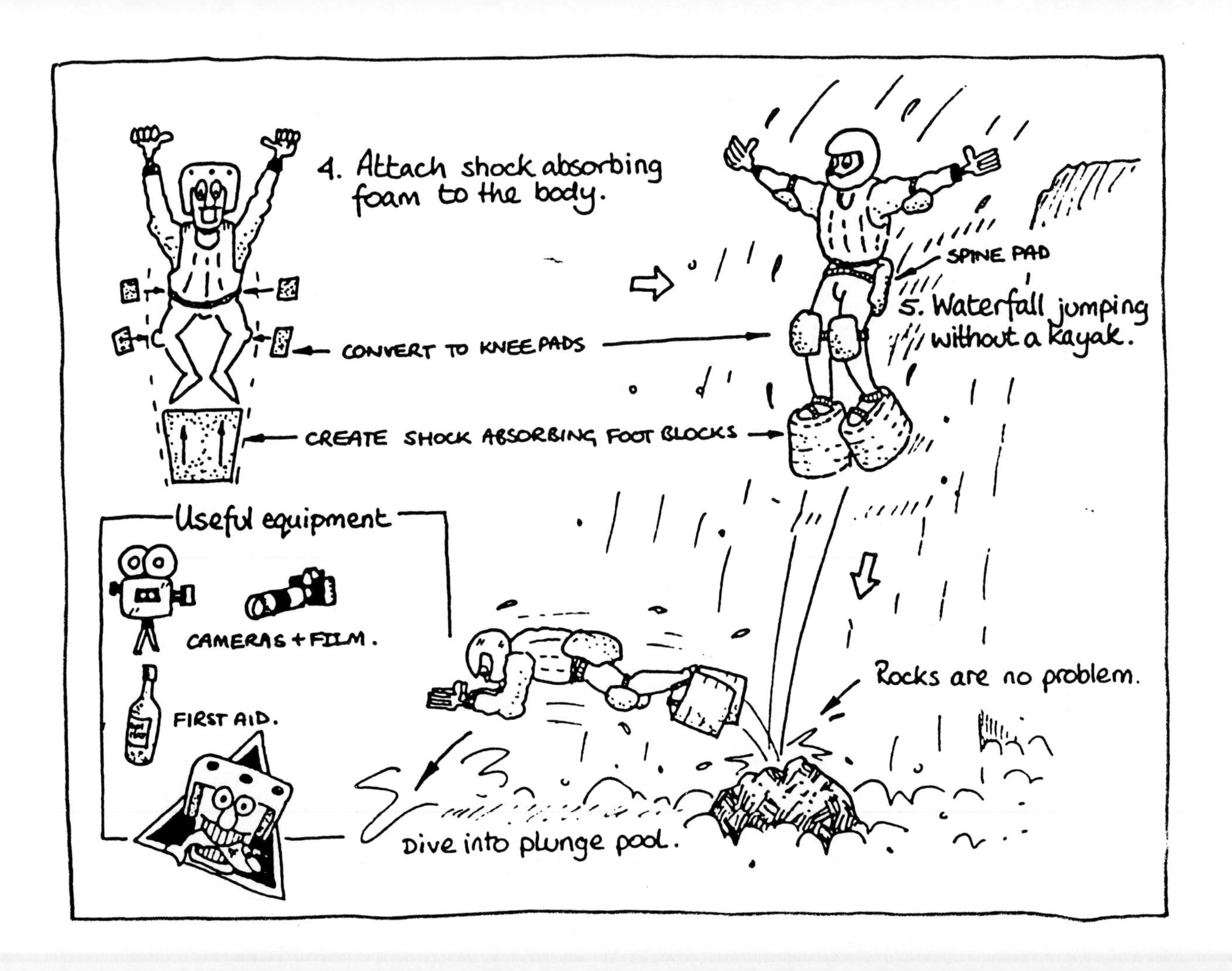
4. Attach shock absorbing foam to the body.
CONVERT TO KNEE PADS
CREATE SHOCK ABSORBING FOOT BLOCKS
SPINE PAD
5. Waterfall jumping without a kayak.
Useful equipment
CAMERAS + FILM.
FIRST AID.
Rocks are no problem.
Dive into plunge pool.

TECHNIQUE: EASING THE CARRY DOWN

TECHNIQUE. HIDING FROM THE RAPIDS

TECHNIQUE. THE WRONG FOOTING

TECHNIQUE. ACCURACY IS ESSENTIAL

·TECHNIQUE·SPEAK·

A familiar pose after a hard day on the river, this means "do not disturb, I'm mellowing out...".

This gesture is often given by those people who are left holding the throw-bag as their colleague attempts an unrunnable fall...

FOXY©.

The familiar breast stroke action used to indicate to kayakers on the water that someone is swimming

This is usually greeted by loud cheers and further encouragement for the victim.

FOXY©.

A subsequent gesture as his unwitting colleague gets well and truly trashed and he is helpless and too horrified to look!

FOXY©.

A familiar sight in the UK or in the Antartic, this indicates that the water is far too cold to roll in, let alone swim and that he should of stayed at home.

FOXY©.

A typical exaggeration of how he managed to ride the largest stopper in the universe and survive!

FOXY©.

'The Stopper was this high' an excuse to hide the fact that it was a very tiny stopper that capsized him! A remarkable similarity to the fishermans 'one that got away', ie: no one else saw it.

"Thumbs up" or 'O.K.' a universal sign with a multitude of meanings: For example;

a) 'It's o.k. come on down!

b) 'It's your turn'..... or more commonly for those with a warped sense of humour

c) (I wouldn't run this) It looks ok to me.

d) A signal often given from the safety of the bank by a sadist, having seen one person just escape from a fall with his life barely intact he signals the next unwitting victim down for a life threatening experience.

FOXY©.

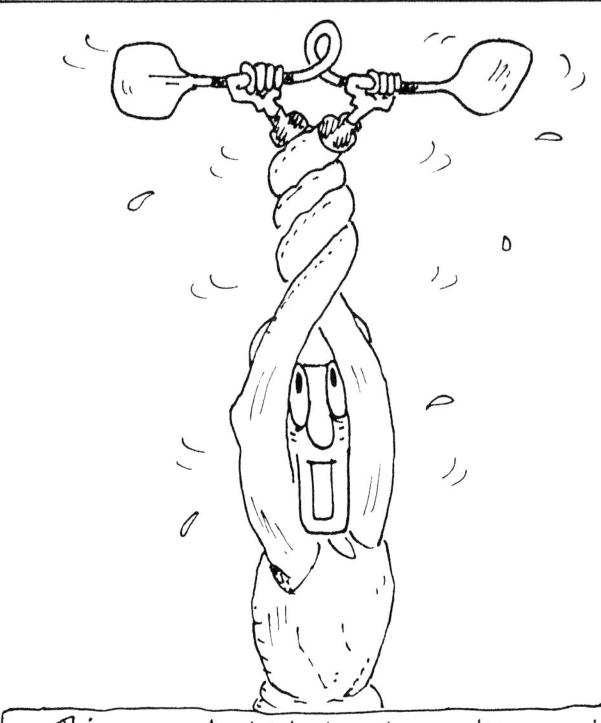

This unusual sight has two possible meanings; either, A) Watch out for the whirlpool or B) the kayaker has just hit a whirlpool and is attempting to unwind.

FOXY©.

...a local 'hair boater' (mirrored shades) describes an endo on Pine Creek.... ...which means he failed to penetrate the hole! [REF: Boaters guide to Rivers of the South West]

FoxY©.

SQUIRTECH

Famous Photo's: ...squirting....

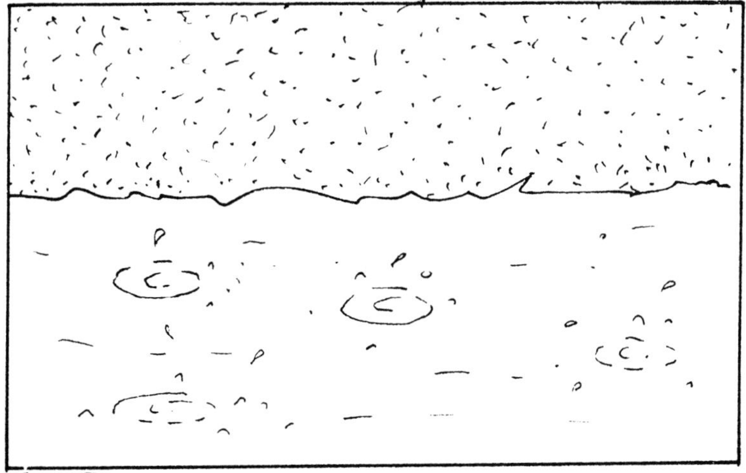

The only way is up! * Mystery move disorientation.

The unwelcome Squirt boat pops up.....!

Yes folks, we fit the paddler to the boat at no extra cost!
SQUIRT SERVICES Inc.
SQUIRT SERVICES Inc
...give me more!...
FOXY©91

An Amazon Mystery move....

RIVER RATS ...Its a Mystery...

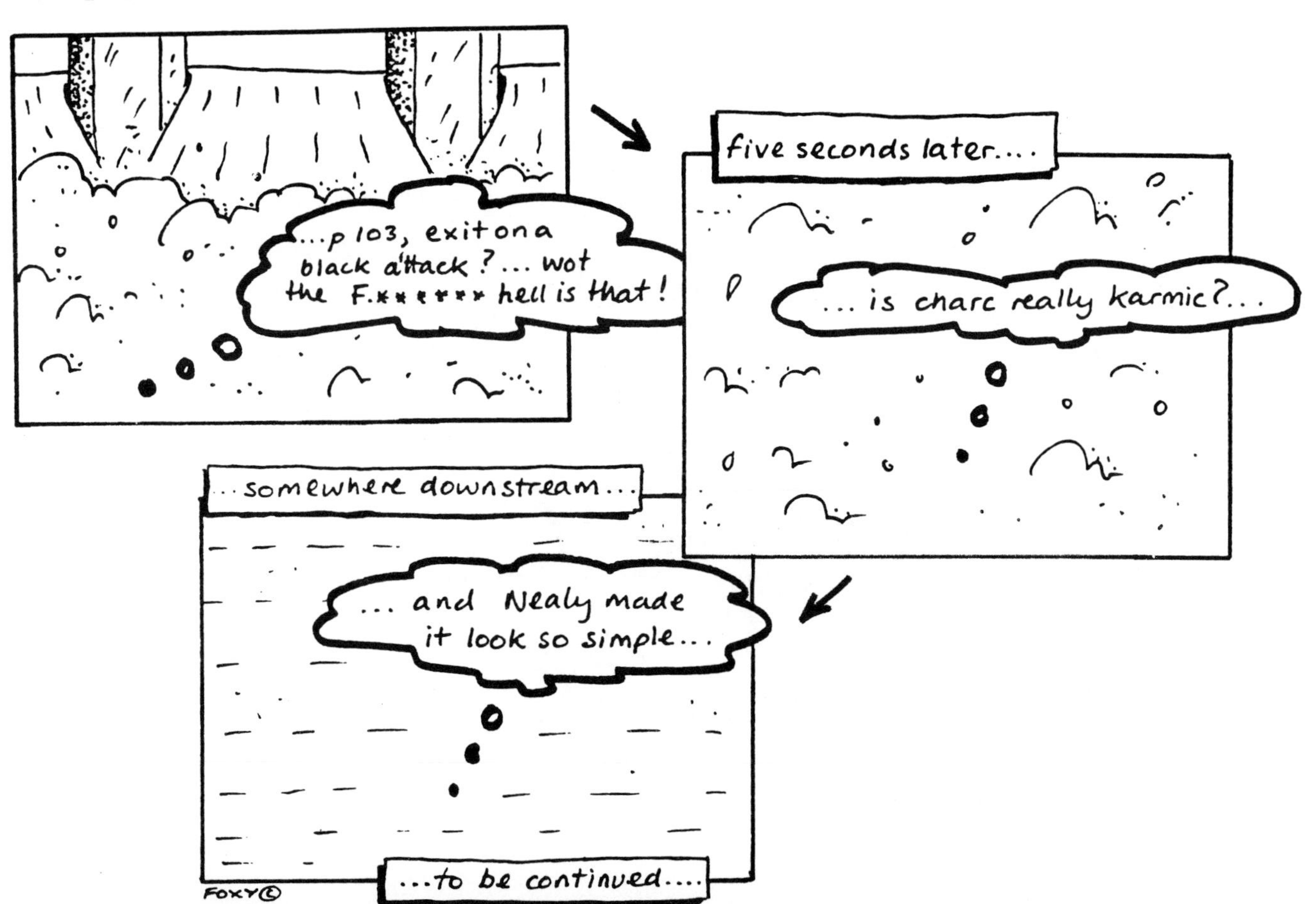
...p 103, exit on a black attack ?... wot the F.****** hell is that !
five seconds later....
... is charc really karmic?...
...somewhere downstream...
... and Nealy made it look so simple...
...to be continued....
FOXY©

Christmas Myths #1
no more smelly reindeers,
smokey chimneys
or screaming kids..
...just surf, sun
and fun for
another 364 days!
FOXY©

...how we would have evolved if paddles hadn't been invented...

On another Planet....

...a meeting of like minds...